Road Transport Rec

Road Rollers

Paul Gladford

Introduction

First published in 2019

British Library Cataloguing in Publication Data

A catalogue record for this book is available from the British Library.

ISBN 978 1 85794 553 9

Silver Link Publishing Ltd
The Trundle
Ringstead Road
Great Addington
Kettering
Northants NN14 4BW

Tel/Fax: 01536 330588
email: sales@nostalgiacollection.com
Website: www.nostalgiacollection.com

Printed and bound in the Czech Republic

Title page: **Marshall** 12 ton roller 88096 passes the remains of the Cornish South Wheal Towan copper mine at Porthtowan.

The development of the steam roller by Thomas Aveling in 1867 'paved' the way for the future of mechanical transport in Britain, initially with steam traction engines then, in the early 20th century, the internal-combustion-engined cars and vehicles that led to the end of horse-drawn transport. Horses and their large wheeled carts were more able to travel on the uneven highways, but the heavier mechanically propelled vehicles required a more substantial firm and smooth base over which to move.

The name of Aveling & Porter, steam engineers from Rochester in Kent, became synonymous with steam rollers, the brass 'Prancing Horse' emblem of Kent and the brass plate carrying the motto 'Invicta' proudly attached to the headstock of every steam roller produced. However, Aveling & Porter did not have the monopoly of steam roller manufacture – other traction engine manufacturers diversified into roller production, while a limited number of companies only produced steam rollers.

The basis design of the steam roller changed little over the years, weighing anything from 4 to 15 tons, although tandem and tri-tandem rollers were experimented with. With the coming of finer and lighter road materials such as asphalt and bitumen, the conventional roller left depressions in these hot materials when it stopped for a while to change from forward to reverse and vice versa, so quick reversing was a necessity. The Wallis Advance roller, having a double-cylinder compound engine, could be reversed almost instantaneously, and it also had smaller and wider rear wheels, which were independent of each other and therefore adapted to the road camber a lot better than the standard roller.

With the onset of the internal combustion engine it was inevitable that the era of the steam-powered roller would come to and end, but Aveling-Barford continued with the production of steam rollers until 1950, and it was not until the 1970s that the last steam rollers were withdrawn from commercial use.

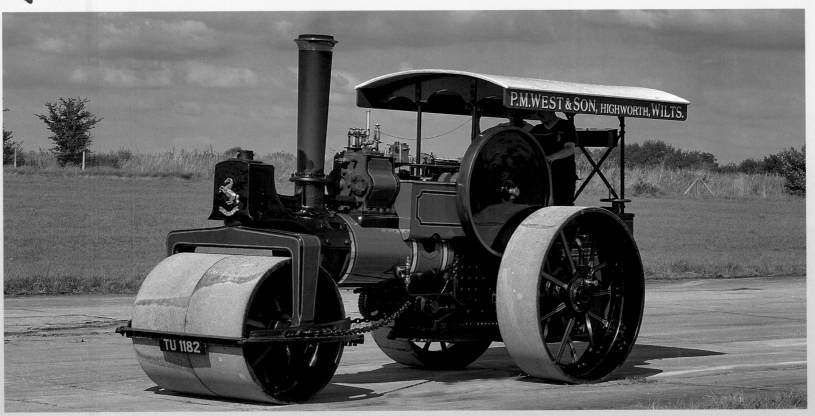

Aveling & Porter 10-ton single-cylinder No 11446, built in 1926, is the archetypal engine that everyone recognises as a 'steam roller'.

Aveling-Barford was formed in 1934 after an amalgamation with Aveling & Porter and continued production of steam rollers until 1950. Set against the backdrop of an Aveling-Barford show stand is 10-ton roller No AE 998, built in 1943.

Armstrong-Whitworth 10-ton roller No 10R2, built in 1923, is one of only seven surviving examples from this manufacturer.

Above: **Aveling & Porter** Single-cylinder 10-ton roller No 8290, built in 1914 and still in work-a-day condition, receives some attention to the fire on the road to Shrewsbury in Shropshire.

Right: **Aveling & Porter** R10 roller No 5590, built in 1904, is seen at Berkeley Castle. This roller was driven by Sid James in the film *The Titfield Thunderbolt*.

Aveling & Porter *Emma*, 10-ton compound roller No 9166 formerly working for Hereford County Council, simmers in the stable yard at Eastnor Castle, Herefordshire.

Right: **Garrett** No 34084 *The Baroness*, a 10-ton roller built in 1922, arrives at the Fairford rally field towing a living van and water cart.

Below: **Aveling & Porter** No 5853, an 8-ton roller built in 1905, has been fitted with smooth rubber tyres over the rolls and is unusually painted crimson.

Trotter This 1-ton vertical-boiler roller was built by Arthur Trotter in 1933 for rolling the paths around his estate.

Marshall Compound 10-ton roller No 75408, built in 1922 for the Isle of Man Highways Board, is seen rolling a driveway near Castletown, Isle of Man.

Aveling & Porter No 6165, a 10-ton compound roller, makes light work of the climb from Porthtowan, even towing a living van.

Wallis & Steevens Advance roller No 7933 levels the top dressing prior to the final rolling.

Above left: **Marshall** No 87125 is an unusual vertical-boiler tandem roller built in 1933.

Left: **Bromovsky, Schulz & Sohr** This was an Austrian steam roller builder, and this 1904-built 13-ton example is visiting the Great Dorset Steam Fair.

Above: **Fowler** No 19481, a 12-ton compound roller, has since been converted to a showman's tractor.

Right: **Wallis & Steevens** Due to its diminutive size, 5-ton roller No 2660 would be used only as a patching roller.

Below: **Aveling & Porter** No 11467, an 8-ton compound roller, pauses for photographs in the Herefordshire village of Eastnor after roading from Malvern.

Left: **Ruston & Hornsby** 12-ton roller No 114059 recreates a common scenario from times past, moving to another rolling contract towing a Bomford & Evershed living van.

Above: **Aveling & Porter** No 12270, a 1929-built single-speed 'F' Type, is preserved in the Highway Museum, Pilmatalawa, Sri Lanka.

Right: **Mann** No 1145 is an unusual patching roller from 1919 with two steerable front rolls and one full-width rear roll.

Below: **Aveling & Porter** 8-ton roller No 10905 of 1924 passes over the River Weaver at the Acton Swing Bridge.

Above: **Babcock & Wilcox** 6-ton roller No 95/4009 was built by Clayton & Shuttleworth, which was owned by Babcock & Wilcox at the time.

Right: **Aveling & Porter** 12-ton roller No 5683 has been seemingly abandoned in the undergrowth on a farm in Warwickshire.

Wallis & Steevens Advance 10-ton rollers Nos 7905 *Tomboy* and 8082 *City of Worcester* stand sentinel at the entrance to the Eastnor Castle courtyard.

Above: **Fowler** 8-ton roller No 21629, owned by the Hockley Heath Steam Association, is seen at Wellesbourne Water Mill.

Above right: **Wallis & Steevens** Simplicity 3-ton roller No 7936 one of the smallest commercial rollers produced and unusual in having an inclined boiler.

Right: **Aveling & Porter** rollers form part of this interesting road-making display at the Great Dorset Steam Fair.

Left: **Aveling & Porter** No 7632 *Betsy* was seen by millions on TV when owned by steeplejack, the late Fred Dibnah.

Right: **Fowler** An unidentified roller owned by Pakistan Railways works in the station yard at Wazirabad, Pakistan, in 1982.

Burrell 10-ton roller No 4012 *Ventongimps*, built in 1925, poses in the village of Offchurch in Warwickshire.

Wallis & Steevens Advance roller No 8034 awaits some attention at a private location.

Left: **Marshall** No 74399, a 10-ton roller, heads for Chappel and Wakes Colne in Essex.

Above: **Ruston & Hornsby** No 52694 has had its working life extended by the replacement of the cylinder and motion with a power unit from a Nuffield tractor.

Left: **Aveling Barford** No AC 604, built towards the end of steam roller production in 1937, has little trouble climbing the hill out of Welford-on-Avon.

Right: **Aveling & Porter** No 4872, built in 1901, compacts freshly laid Cotswold stone at Stanway House in the Cotswolds.

Left: **Marshall** No 70425, a 6-ton single-cylinder 'S' Type steam roller fitted with two-tine Allen scarifier, is preserved in the Highway Museum, Pilmatalawa, Sri Lanka.

Right: **Wallis & Steevens** Advance roller No 8005, built in 1929, is exhibited in as-found condition at the Fairford Rally.

Burrell No 3985, a substantial looking 8-ton roller, is exhibited at the Great Dorset Steam Fair.

Fowler Like most manufacturers, Fowler exported many of its products. This compound roller, No 16480 from 1925, survives at the time of writing in the town of Messina in South Africa.

Aveling & Porter No 8717, a 15 ton example, has little problem in compacting the hardcore base of the newly laid road.

Right: **Marshall** No 74450 *Sallie*, an 8-ton roller built in 1921, pauses while on a road run in Cheshire.

Left: **Aveling & Porter** 'C' Type roller No 11956, built in 1927, is seen in the unlikely setting of the farm used as a location in the *Heartbeat* TV series.

Above: **John Allen** This example was rebuilt from Fowler roller No 8111 in 1898 by John Allen Ltd, Oxford.

Left: **Marshall** Universal No 87260 is similar in concept to the Wallis & Steevens Advance roller, having two high-pressure cylinders and no flywheel, allowing for a quick change in direction.

Right: **Robey** Tandem roller No 42129 of 1924 tackles the steep climb up 'Engine Hill' from Porthtowan while taking part in the WSES road run.

Left: **Aveling & Porter** No 14181 *Highland Maid* is exhibited in a typical road-making scene.

Right: **Marshall** This unidentified roller is preserved in the grounds of the railway golf club in Lahore, Pakistan.

Aveling & Porter 'F' Type 10-ton roller No 10824 is resplendent in crimson livery at Buckfastleigh station in Devon.

Aveling & Porter No 10906 *Cinderella*, an 'E' Type 10-ton roller, is on an autumn end-of-season road run in Shropshire.

Marshall Roller No 88876 is in the company of a narrow-gauge Garratt-hauled train and a wagon hauled by a team of oxen at the Sandstone Estates in Free State, South Africa.

Aveling & Porter 10-ton 'E' Class roller No 10556 is seen against the backdrop of Belvoir Castle.

Aveling & Porter This motor road roller powered by a single-cylinder oil engine was built in the 1920s and exported to Sri Lanka.

Aveling Barford No AH 368, built in 1947 and exported to Sri Lanka, was one of the last steam rollers produced in the UK.

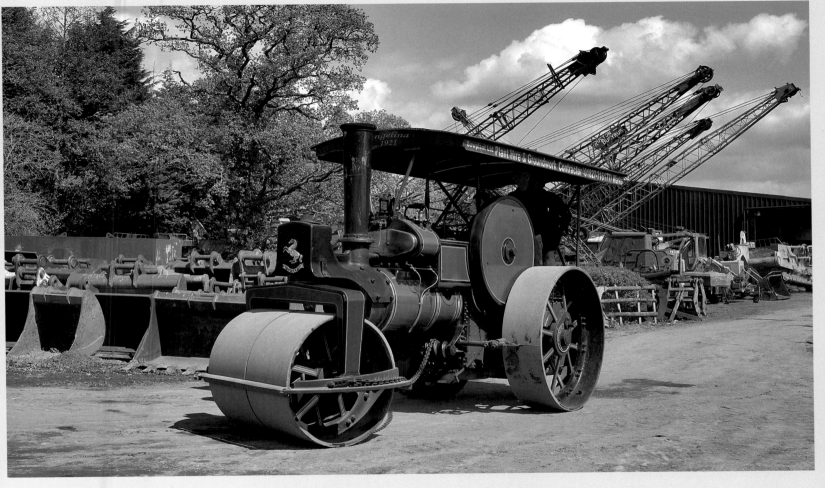

Aveling & Porter 10-ton compound roller No 10073, built in 1922, stands among a collection of other civil engineering equipment at Astwood Bank.

Aveling & Porter Work-stained 10-ton roller No 7600 arrives towing a living van and water cart, a scene typical of the working days of a steam roller when moving between contracts.

Aveling & Porter 6-ton roller No 10431, former Eddison fleet No 429, forms part of a road-making demonstration at the Great Dorset Steam Fair.

Fowler Compound 10-ton roller No 20122, while not employed commercially, still serves a useful purpose compacting a stone car park in Sherbourne, Warwickshire.